THE TWIG ON THE BOUGH

THE TREE IN THE WOOD

Book 3

THE TWIG
ON THE BOUGH

Poems chosen by

RAYMOND O'MALLEY

& DENYS THOMPSON

Decorations by Julia Ball

THE TREE IN THE WOOD: BOOK 3

FRANKLIN WATTS, INC.
575 Lexington Avenue
New York, N.Y. 10022

Copyright © Chatto and Windus Ltd 1966
Library of Congress Catalog Card Number: 68-19243

Published 1966 by
Chatto and Windus Ltd, London
First American Publication 1968
by Franklin Watts, Inc.
1 2 3 4

Printed in the U.S.A.

CONTENTS

§ 1

§ 2

§ 8

The egg was in the nest,
The nest was on the twig,
The twig was on the bough,
The bough was on the tree,
The tree was in the wood:
And the green grass grew all round,
around, around,
And the green grass grew all round.

Scarecrow

Hi, Mister Scarecrow!
Well, bless *me*,
Ain't you a funny
Sight to see!
Why, *I* know *you*
Well as can be—
Your body is a broomstick
He, he, he!
Your gloves once belonged
To the Parson's ma!
Your hat was the Farmer's,
Ha, ha, ha!
Your trousers were the Cowman's,
Your coat used to go
With Gaffer Green to market,
Ho, ho, ho!
Hi, Mister Scarecrow!
You may be
A scare for crows,
But you can't scare *me*!

ELEANOR FARJEON

The Ostrich

The ostrich roams the great Sahara.
Its mouth is wide, its neck is narra.
It has such long and lofty legs,
I'm glad it sits to lay its eggs.

OGDEN NASH

Sweet Betsy

Do you remember sweet Betsy from Pike?
Crossed the big mountains with her lover, Ike,
With two yoke of oxen, a big yellow dog,
A cross Shanghai rooster, and one spotted hog.

They soon reached the desert, where Betsy gave out.
Down on the sand she lay rolling about.
Ike he gazed at her with sobs and with sighs:
'Won't you get up, Betsy, ye'll get sand in your eyes.'

The Shanghai ran off, and the cattle all died;
The last piece of bacon that morning was fried.
Ike got discouraged and Betsy got mad;
The dog wagged his tail and looked wonderfully sad.

The Hayloft

Through the pleasant meadow-side
   The grass grew shoulder-high,
Till the shining scythes went far and wide
   And cut it down to dry.

These green and sweetly smelling crops
   They led in waggons home;
And they piled them here in mountain tops
   For mountaineers to roam.

Here is Mount Clear, Mount Rusty-Nail,
   Mount Eagle and Mount High—
The mice that in these mountains dwell,
   No happier are than I!

O what a joy to clamber there,
   O what a place for play,
With the sweet, the dim, the dusty air,
   The happy hills of hay.

R. L. STEVENSON

Things to Remember

The buttercups in May,
The wild rose on the spray,
The poppy in the hay,

The primrose in the dell,
The freckled foxglove bell,
The honeysuckle's smell

Are things I would remember
When cheerless, raw November
Makes room for dark December.

JAMES REEVES

The Robin

When up aloft
I fly and fly,
I see in pools
The shining sky,
And a happy bird
Am I, am I!

When I descend
Toward the brink
I stand and look
And stop and drink
And bathe my wings,
And chink, and prink.

When winter frost
Makes earth as steel,
I search and search
But find no meal,
And most unhappy
Then I feel.

But when it lasts,
And snows still fall,
I get to feel
No grief at all,
For I turn to a cold, stiff
Feathery ball!

THOMAS HARDY

Two Old Bachelors

Two old Bachelors
   were living in one house;
One caught a Muffin,
   the other caught a Mouse.

Said he who caught the Muffin
   to him who caught the Mouse,
'This happens just in time,
   for we've nothing in the house!'

Said he who caught the Mouse
   to him who caught the Muffin,
'We might cook this little Mouse,
   if we only had some Stuffin'!'

They borrowed two large Onions,
   but no Sage was to be found
In the Shops, or in the Market,
   or in all the Gardens round.

And when they reached their house, they found
   (besides their want of Stuffin'),
The Mouse had fled; and previously,
   had eaten up the Muffin.

EDWARD LEAR

In the Snow

Hear how my friend the robin sings!
  That little hunchback in the snow,
As it comes down as fast as rain.
  The air is cold, the wind doth blow,
And still his heart can feel no pain.

And I, with heart as light as his,
  And to my ankles deep in snow,
Hold up a fist as cold as Death's,
  And into it I laugh and blow—
I laugh and blow my life's warm breath.

W. H. DAVIES

Winter Rain

Every valley drinks.
  Every dell and hollow:
Where the kind rain sinks and sinks,
  Green of Spring will follow.

Yet a lapse of weeks
  Buds will burst their edges,
Strip their wool-coats, glue-coats, streaks,
  In the woods and hedges;

Weave a bower of love
  For birds to meet each other,
Weave a canopy above
  Nest and egg and mother.

16

But for fattening rain
   We should have no flowers,
Never a bud or leaf again
   But for soaking showers;

Never a mated bird
   In the rocking tree-tops,
Never indeed a flock or herd
   To graze upon the lea-crops.

Lambs so woolly white,
   Sheep the sun-bright leas on,
They could have no grass to bite
   But for rain in season.

We should find no moss
   In the shadiest places,
Find no waving meadow grass
   Pied with broad-eyed daisies:

But miles of barren sand,
   With never a son or daughter,
Not a lily on the land,
   Or a lily on the water.

CHRISTINA ROSSETTI

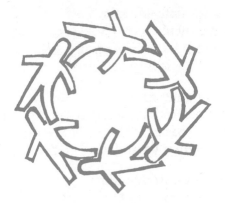

Mister Fox

A fox went out in a hungry plight,
And he begged of the moon to give him light,
For he'd many miles to trot that night,
  Before he could reach his den O!

And first he came to a farmer's yard,
Where the ducks and geese declared it hard
That their nerves should be shaken and their rest be marr'd,
  By the visit of Mister Fox O!

He took the grey goose by the sleeve;
Says he, 'Madam Goose, and by your leave,
I'll take you away without reprieve,
  And carry you home to my den O!'

He seized the black duck by the neck,
And swung her over across his back;
The black duck cried out, 'Quack! Quack! Quack!'
  With her legs hanging dangling down O!

Then old Mrs. Slipper-slopper jump'd out of bed,
And out of the window she popp'd her head,
Crying, 'John, John, John, the grey goose is gone,
    And the fox is away to his den O!'

Then John he went up to the top of the hill,
And he blew a blast both loud and shrill;
Says the fox, 'That is very pretty music—still
    I'd rather be in my den O!'

At last the fox got home to his den;
To his dear little foxes, eight, nine, ten,
Says he, 'You're in luck, here's a good fat duck,
    With her legs hanging dangling down O!'

He then sat down with his hungry wife;
They did very well without fork or knife;
They'd never ate better in all their life,
    And the little ones pick'd the bones O!

The Months

January brings the snow,
Makes our feet and fingers glow.
February brings the rain,
Thaws the frozen lake again.
March brings breezes loud and shrill,
Stirs the dancing daffodil.
April brings the primrose sweet,
Scatters daisies at our feet.
May brings flocks of pretty lambs,
Skipping by their fleecy dams.
June brings tulips, lilies, roses,
Fills the children's hands with posies.
Hot July brings cooling showers,
Apricots and gillyflowers.
August brings the sheaves of corn,
Then the harvest home is borne.
Warm September brings the fruit,
Sportsmen then begin to shoot.
Fresh October brings the pheasant,
Then to gather nuts is pleasant.
Dull November brings the blast,
Then the leaves are whirling fast.
Chill December brings the sleet,
Blazing fire and Christmas treat.

SARA COLERIDGE

dams, mothers

20

The Carter and His Team

I was once a bold fellow, and went with a team,
And all my delight was in keeping them clean,
With brushes and curries I'd show their bright colour
And the name that they gave me was 'a hearty good fellow.'

As every evening I went to my bed
The thought of my horses came into my head,
I rose in the morning to give them their meat
As soon as I got my shoes on my feet.

The first was a white horse, as white as the milk;
The next was a grey horse, as soft as the silk;
The next was a brown horse, as sleek as a mole;
The last was a great horse, as black as a coal.

As I went a-driving all on the highway,
When light went my load, then I fed them with hay;
And watered them well when we came to a pond.
(And after they've drunk, boys, go steady beyond.)

My feet they grew weary as I walked by their side;
I said to my mate, 'I will get up and ride.'
And as I was riding I made a new song,
And as I did sing it, you must learn it along.

curries, special combs for grooming   *meat*, food

Seasons

Oh the cheerful budding-time!
    When thorn-hedges turn to green,
When new leaves of elm and lime
    Cleave and shed their winter screen.

Oh the gorgeous blossom-days!
    When broad flag-flowers drink and blow;
In and out in summer-blaze
    Dragon-flies flash to and fro.

Oh the shouting harvest-weeks!
    Mother earth grown fat with sheaves
Thrifty gleaner finds who seeks;
    Russet-golden pomp of leaves.

Oh the starving winter-lapse!
    Ice-bound, hunger-pinched and dim;
Dormant roots recall their saps,
    Empty nests show black and grim.

CHRISTINA ROSSETTI

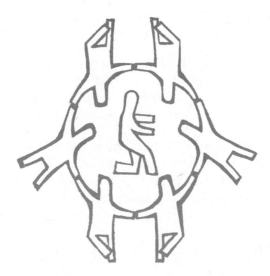

The Toad

As I was running down the road,
I met an agéd wrinkled toad
Hobbling along to her abode.

It seemed to give her such a scare
To meet me on her journey there,
She looked the picture of despair.

Betwixt fear, anger, and surprise
She puffed herself to such a size,
I scarcely could believe my eyes.

As all that I could do or say
Seemed but to add to her dismay,
I wished her well, and ran away.

E. L. M. KING

Betty Botter

Betty Botter bought some butter,
But, she said, the butter's bitter;
If I put it in my batter
It will make my batter bitter,
But a bit of better butter,
That would make my batter better,
So she bought a bit of butter
Better than her bitter butter,
And she put it in her batter
And the batter was not bitter.
So t'was better Betty Botter
Bought a bit of better butter.

The Kitten

The kitten sleeps. Her coat is black and satiny and
    soft as silk;
She lies upon her side and dreams of unlocked
    dairies full of milk,
Of fish fresh caught and all for her, and pails and
    pails of yellow cream.
She gives a long tremulous purr and goes on with her
    lovely dream.
Her coat is like a starless night, and green as beryls
    are her eyes;
She is a playful little cat, and loves to chase blue
    butterflies;
She is a naughty little cat, and sometimes, when she
    sees the late
Delivered milk upon the step, she finds the temptation
    too great . . .
And we will come and find her there, her body sunk
    in the great armchair,
Her face a mask of innocence, no drop of milk upon
    her hair.

We know she often steals the milk, but yet we cannot
   punish her:
She is so cheeky and so sweet; such amber eyes, such
   coal black fur;
Such an inquisitive little nose, with tip of white; and
   snowy paws;
Her tail is black and without speck; but there is white
   along her jaws.
She loves to watch the glowing fire; and when she's
   awake, she can be
Quite the naughtiest little cat that I do ever wish to
   see!
But now she sleeps, her tail hung low, her body limp
   in the big arm-chair,
And I will have her sleeping so, and drop a kiss upon
   her hair.

ELIZABETH DU PREEZ

'Please to Remember'

Here am I,
A poor old Guy:
Legs in a bonfire,
Head in the sky,

Shoeless my toes,
Wild stars behind,
Smoke in my nose,
And my eye-peeps blind;

Old hat, old straw—
In this disgrace;
While the wildfire gleams
On a mask for face.

Ay, all I am made of
Only trash is;
And soon—soon,
Will be dust and ashes.

WALTER DE LA MARE

Robin-a-Thrush

O, Robin-a-Thrush he married a wife,
  With a hoppety, moppety mow now!
She proved to be the plague of his life,
  With a hig-jig-jiggety, ruffety petticoat,
  Robin-a-Thrush cries mow now!

She never gets up till twelve o'clock,
Puts on her gown and above it her smock.

She sweeps the house but once a year,
The reason is that brooms are dear.

She milks her cows but once a week,
And that's what makes her butter sweet.

The butter she made in an old man's boot;
For want of a churn she clapped in her foot.

Her cheese when made was put on the shelf,
And it never was turned till it turned of itself.

It turned and turned till it walked on the floor,
It stood upon legs and walked to the door.

It walked till it came to Banbury Fair;
The dame followed after upon a grey mare.

This song it was made for gentlemen,
If you want any more you must sing it again!

Dashing away with the Smoothing-iron

'Twas on a Monday morning
    That I beheld my darling;
    She looked so neat and charming
    In every high degree;
She looked so neat and nimble, O,
Washing of her linen, O!
    Dashing away with the smoothing-iron,
    Dashing away with the smoothing-iron,
    Dashing away with the smoothing-iron
    She stole my heart away.

'Twas on a Tuesday morning
    That I beheld my darling;
    She looked so neat and charming
    In every high degree;
She looked so neat and nimble, O,
Hanging out her linen, O!
    Dashing away with the smoothing-iron,
    Dashing away with the smoothing-iron,
    Dashing away with the smoothing-iron
    She stole my heart away.

'Twas on a Wednesday morning . . .
She looked so neat and nimble, O,
Starching of her linen, O! . . .

'Twas on a Thursday morning . . .
She looked so neat and nimble, O,
Ironing of her linen, O! . . .

'Twas on a Friday morning . . .
She looked so neat and nimble, O,
Folding of her linen, O! . . .

'Twas on a Saturday morning . . .
She looked so neat and nimble, O,
Airing of her linen, O! . . .

'Twas on a Sunday morning
    That I beheld my darling;
    She looked so neat and charming
    In every high degree;
She looked so neat and nimble, O,
Wearing of her linen, O!
    Dashing away with the smoothing-iron,
    Dashing away with the smoothing-iron,
    Dashing away with the smoothing-iron
    She stole my heart away.

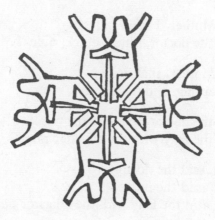

White Fields

In the winter time we go
Walking in the fields of snow;

Where there is no grass at all;
Where the top of every wall

Every fence and every tree,
Is as white as white can be.

Pointing out the way we came,
—Every one of them the same—

All across the fields there be
Prints in silver filigree;
And our mothers always know,
By the footprints in the snow,
Where it is the children go.

JAMES STEPHENS

Mother, Mother!

Mother, Mother, I feel sick:
Send for the doctor, quick, quick, quick!

Mother, Mother, shall I die?
No, my darling, and do not cry.

Send for the doctor, send for the nurse,
Send for the lady with the alligator purse!

Penicillin, said the doctor;
Penicillin, said the nurse;
Penicillin said the lady with the alligator purse. . . .

An Odd Fellow

There was one who was famed for the number of things
   He forgot when he entered the ship:
His umbrella, his watch, all his jewels and rings,
   And the clothes he had bought for the trip.

He had forty-two boxes, all carefully packed,
   With his name painted clearly on each;
But, since he omitted to mention the fact,
   They were all left behind on the beach.

The loss of his clothes hardly mattered, because
   He had seven coats on when he came,
With three pair of boots—but the worst of it was,
   He had wholly forgotten his name.

He would answer to 'Hi!' or to any loud cry,
   Such as 'Fry me!' or 'Fritter my wig!'
To 'What-you-may-call-um!' or 'What-was-his-name!'
   But especially 'Thing-um-a-jig!'

While, for those who preferred a more forcible word,
   He had different names from these:
His intimate friends call him 'Candle-ends',
   And his enemies 'Toasted-cheese'.

LEWIS CARROLL

A Thanksgiving to God, for His House

Lord, thou hast given me a cell
   Wherein to dwell;
A little house, whose humble roof
   Is weather-proof;
Under the spars of which I lie
   Both soft, and dry. . . .

Like as my parlour, so my hall
   And kitchen's small:
Some brittle sticks of thorn or briar
   Make me a fire,
Close by whose living coal I sit,
   And glow like it. . . .

Thou mak'st my teeming hen to lay
   Her egg each day:
All these, and better Thou dost send
   Me to this end,
That I should render, for my part,
   A thankful heart.

ROBERT HERRICK

Useful Things

I'd like so very much to have
Some of the useful things
That lucky birds and beasts have got,
And first of all their wings;

For then into the apple-tree
I should not need to climb,
And graze my legs and tear my frock
In getting down each time.

Then when the flies are troublesome
I'd like to have a tail,
And when I'm battling with the wasps,
The beetle's coat of mail.

When I am bathing in the sea
And find it hard to float,
I'd like to borrow from the duck
Her webs and oily coat.

For thus provided I could live
On land, in air, or sea,
And fly and flap, and fight and float,
Just as it suited me.

E. L. M. KING

On These November Evenings

On these November evenings
We walk home quietly.
The others call, 'Goodbye, Ann!'
And hurry indoors for tea.

But David and I run out
To sit on the rails
And watch the passing traffic
Until the light fails.

We watch the heavy lorries,
Each with its swinging load
Of rods and iron piping,
Move down the by-pass road.

David on the bus-stop railing
Does antics crying, 'Ann,
Can you do backward-twizzles?'
Of course I can!

Sometimes a shouting gipsy,
Her face hard and sour,
Goes by, drops from her basket
A chrysanthemum flower.

And sometimes Ted and Alan
Come running. They can't wait:
They're off to meet their father
Outside the factory gate.

Or John and Betty Savage.
'Down to the shop!' cries John.
'See you at pictures to-morrow!'
And they both hurry on.

We wait. The yellow vapour
Which has warmed the air all day
Thickens into a darkness
Over the River Cray.

Till all at once the road-lamps
Shine white overhead;
And David's face beneath them
Is weird and ghastly-dead.

'Look, Dave! The factory-windows!
Don't all the lights look gold?'
But David he sits quiet;
And the rail grows cold.

We watch the moving head-lamps.
And now in the long line
There comes the lighted number
Of a 3-2-9.

It slides to a standstill:
The workmen push and shout,
Struggling past the conductor
To be first out.

Then a sudden voice says, 'Hallo, dear!'
And from the throbbing 'bus
Gets Mother, with her smile and her basket,
And a cake for us!

JOHN WALSH

The Deaf Old Woman

'Old woman, old woman, will you go a-shearing?'
'Speak a little louder, sir, I'm very hard of hearing.'

'Old woman, old woman, will you go a-gleaning?'
'Speak a little louder, sir, I cannot tell your meaning.'

'Old woman, old woman, shall we go a-walking?'
'Speak a little louder, sir, I think I hear you talking.'

'Old woman, old woman, shall I love you dearly?'
'Now at last I hear you, sir—I hear you very clearly.'

The Deserted House

There's no smoke in the chimney,
  And the rain beats on the floor;
There's no glass in the window,
  There's no wood in the door;
The heather grows behind the house,
  And the sand lies before.

No hand hath trained the ivy,
  The walls are grey and bare;
The boats upon the sea sail by,
  Nor ever tarry there.
No beast of the field comes nigh,
  Nor any bird of the air.

MARY COLERIDGE

Rats in the Larder

The rats by night such mischief did,
Betty was every morning chid:
They undermined whole sides of bacon,
Her cheese was sapped, her tarts were taken,
Her pasties, fenced with thickest paste,
Were all demolished and laid waste.
She cursed the cat for want of duty,
Who left her foes a constant booty.

JOHN GAY

chid, blamed

The Vixen

Among the taller wood with ivy hung,
The old fox plays and dances round her young.
She snuffs and barks if any passes by
And swings her tail and turns prepared to fly.
The horseman hurries by, she bolts to see,
And turns agen, from danger never free.
If any stands she runs among the poles
And barks and snaps and drives them in the holes.
The shepherd sees them and the boy goes by
And gets a stick and progs the hole to try.
They get all still and lie in safety sure,
And out again when everything's secure,
And start and snap at blackbirds bouncing by
To fight and catch the great white butterfly.

JOHN CLARE

Mr. Tom Narrow

A scandalous man
    Was Mr. Tom Narrow,
He pushed his grandmother
    Round in a barrow.
And he called out loud
    As he rang his bell,
'Grannies to sell!
    Old grannies to sell!'

The neighbours said,
    As they passed them by,
'This poor old lady
    We will not buy.
He surely must be
    A mischievous man
To try for to sell
    His own dear Gran.'

'Besides,' said another,
    'If you ask me,
She'd be very small use
    That I can see.'
'You're right,' said a third,
    'And no mistake —
A very poor bargain
    She'd surely make.'

So Mr. Tom Narrow
  He scratched his head,
And he sent his grandmother
  Back to bed;
And he rang his bell
  Through all the town
Till he sold his barrow
  For half a crown.

JAMES REEVES

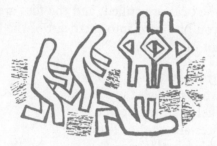

Wisdom

There be four things which are little upon the earth,
But they are exceeding wise:
The ants are a people not strong,
Yet they provide their meat in the summer;
The conies are but a feeble folk,
Yet make they their houses in the rocks;
The locusts have no king,
Yet go they forth all of them by bands;
The lizard taketh hold with her hands,
Yet is she in kings' palaces.

THE BIBLE

conies, rabbits

Winter

The frost is here,
And fuel is dear,
The woods are sear,
And fires burn clear;
The frost is here
And has bitten the heel of the going year.

Bite, frost, bite!
You roll up away from the light
The blue wood-louse, and the plump dormouse,
And the bees are stilled, and the flies are killed,
And you bite hard into the heart of the house,
But not into mine.

Bite, frost, bite!
The woods are all the searer,
The fuel is all the dearer,
The fires are all the clearer,
My spring is all the nearer,
You have bitten into the heart of the earth,
But not into mine.

ALFRED TENNYSON

The Sand Castle

All evening I worked to build me a huge
Castle of sand;
While the gulls' cry and the sea's cry
Drew back from the land.

I toiled and toiled; till there, by the light
Of the hard moon,
A fortress stood, black-shadowed, grim,
Triumphant . . . Soon

They came to fetch me. 'Come now, Jeremy,
It's supper,' they said;
And 'No more play tonight, Jeremy —
It's time for bed.'

But here I'll watch by my bedroom window,
Cold-footed, alone,
Till the full sea comes shining in —
And my castle's gone.

JOHN WALSH

Anne
1702

Queen Anne's dead!
Poor Queen Anne!
If she was plain,
She had a pretty fan,
If she was dull,
She wore a pretty gown,
And almost looked alive
Underneath her crown.

Queen Anne's dead!
Poor plain Anne!
Fold her pretty gown,
Close her pretty fan,
And on her pretty monument
Let nothing else be read
But these plain words:
Queen Anne's dead!

ELEANOR AND HERBERT FARJEON

Riding Gently

There was an Old Person of Ware,
Who rode on the back of a Bear;
   When they asked, 'Does it trot?'
   He said, 'Certainly not!
He's a Moppsikon Floppsikon Bear!'

EDWARD LEAR

A Wedding

The wedding was timed for
  Twelve on the clocks.
The bridegroom was a
  Jack-in-the-box;

The bride a columbine
  Ragged and old,
Found in a car-park at
  Stow-on-the-Wold.

The ring was given,
  The bride was kissed;
The future seemed all
  Love-in-the-mist;

But some of their joy was
  Nipped in the bud;
Each proved a bit of a
  Stick-in-the-mud:

He calls her his muggins,
  His mouse and his mole;
She feeds him on porridge and
  Toad-in-the-hole.

RAYMOND O'MALLEY

43

King John and the Abbot of Canterbury

An ancient story I'll tell you anon,
Of a notable prince, that was called King John;
And he ruled England with main and with might,
For he did great wrong and maintained little right.

And I'll tell you a story, a story so merry,
Concerning the Abbot of Canterbury;
How, through his house-keeping and high renown,
They rode post for him to fair London town.

A hundred men, the King did hear say,
The Abbot kept in his house every day;
And fifty gold chains, without any doubt,
In velvet coats waited the Abbot about.

'How now, Father Abbot, I hear it of thee
Thou keepest a far better house than me,
And for thy house-keeping and high renown,
I fear thou work'st treason against my crown.'

'My Liege,' quoth the Abbot, 'I would it were known,
I never spend nothing but what is my own;
And I trust your Grace will think me not bold
For spending of my own true-gotten gold.'

'Yes, yes, Father Abbot, thy fault it is high,
And now for the same thou needest must die;
For except thou can answer me questions three,
Thy head shall be smitten from thy body.

'And first,' quoth the King, 'when I'm in this stead,
With my crown of gold so fair on my head,
Among all my liege-men so noble of birth,
Thou must tell me to one penny of what I am worth.

'Secondly, tell me, without any doubt,
How soon I may ride the whole world about.
And at the third question thou must not shrink,
But tell me here truly what I do think.' —

'O, these are hard questions for my shallow wit,
Nor I cannot answer your Grace as yet:
But if you will give me but three weeks' space,
I'll do my endeavour to answer your Grace.'

'Now three weeks' space to thee will I give,
And that is the longest time thou hast to live;
For if thou dost not answer my questions three,
Thy lands and thy livings are forfeit to me.'

Away rode the Abbot all sad at that word,
And he rode to Cambridge, and Oxenford;
But never a doctor there was so wise,
That could with his learning an answer devise.

Then home rode the Abbot of comfort so cold,
And he met with his shepherd a-going to fold:
'How now, my lord Abbot, you are welcome home;
What news do you bring us from good King John?'

'Sad news, sad news, shepherd, I must give;
That I have but three days more to live:
For if I do not answer him questions three,
My head will be smitten from my body.

'The first is to tell him there in that stead,
With his crown of gold so fair on his head,
Among all his liege-men so noble of birth,
To within one penny of what he is worth.

'The second, to tell him, without any doubt,
How soon he may ride this whole world about:
And at the third question I must not shrink,
But tell him there truly what he does think.'

'Now cheer up, sire Abbot, did you never hear yet,
That a fool he may teach a wise man wit?
Lend me a horse, and serving-men, and your apparel,
And I'll ride to London to answer your quarrel.

'Nay, frown not, for it hath been told unto me,
I am like your lordship as ever may be:
And if you will but lend me your gown,
There is none that shall know us at fair London town.'—

'Now horses and serving-men thou shalt have,
With sumptuous array most gallant and brave;
With crozier, and mitre, and rochet, and cope,
Fit to appear 'fore our Father and Pope.'

'Now welcome, sire Abbot,' the King he did say,
' 'Tis well thou art come back to keep thy day;
For if thou can answer my questions three,
Thy life and thy living shall both saved be.

'And first, when thou seest me here in this stead,
With my crown of gold so fair on my head,
Among all my liege-men so noble of birth,
Tell me to one penny what I am worth.'

'For thirty pence our Saviour was sold,
Among the false Jews, as I have been told;
And twenty-nine is the worth of thee,
For I think thou art one penny worser than he.'

The King he laughed, and swore by St. Bittel,
'I did not think I had been worth so little!
—Now secondly tell me, without any doubt,
How soon I may ride this whole world about.'

'You must rise with the sun, and ride with the same,
Until the next morning he rises again;
And then your Grace need not make any doubt,
But in twenty-four hours you'll ride it about.'

The King he laughed, and swore by St. John,
'I did not think it could be done so soon!
—Now from the third question thou must not shrink,
But tell me here truly what I do think.'

'Yea, that shall I do, and make your Grace merry:
You think I'm the Abbot of Canterbury;
But I'm his poor shepherd, as plain you may see,
That am come to beg pardon for him and for me.'

The King he laughed, and swore by the Mass,
'I'll make thee Lord Abbot this day in his place!'
'Now nay, my Liege, be not in such speed,
For alack I can neither write nor read.'

'Four nobles a week, then, I will give thee
For this merry jest thou hast shown unto me;
And tell the old Abbot when thou comest home,
Thou hast brought him a pardon from good King John.'

For want of a nail

For want of a nail
  The shoe was lost,
For want of a shoe
  The horse was lost,
For want of a horse
  The rider was lost,
For want of a rider
  The battle was lost,
And all for the want
  Of a horse shoe nail.

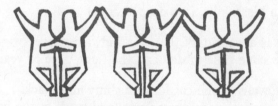

Fairy Entertainment

Be kind and courteous to this gentleman —
Hop in his walks, and gambol in his eyes;
Feed him with apricots and dewberries,
With purple grapes, green figs, and mulberries;
The honey-bags steal from the humble-bees,
And for night-tapers crop their waxen thighs,
And light them at the fiery glow-worm's eyes,
To have my love to bed and to arise;
And pluck the wings from painted butterflies
To fan the moonbeams from his sleeping eyes.
Nod to him, elves, and do him courtesies.

WILLIAM SHAKESPEARE

Frodge-dobbulum

Did you ever see Giant Frodge-dobbulum,
With his double great-toe and his double great-thumb?

Did you ever hear Giant Frodge-dobbulum
Saying *Fa-fe-fi* and *fo-faw-fum*?

He shakes the earth as he walks along,
As deep as the sea, as far as Hong-Kong!

He is a giant and no mistake,
With teeth like the prongs of a garden rake.

Castle Frodge-dobbulum sulked between
Two bleak hills, in a deep ravine.

It was always dark there, and always drear,
The same time of day and the same time of year.

The walls of the castle were slimy and black,
There were dragons in front, and toads at the back.

Spiders there were, and of vampires lots;
Ravens croaked round the chimney-pots.

Seven bull-dogs barked in the hall;
Seven wild cats did caterwaul!

The Giant Frodge-dobbulum got out of bed,
Sighing, 'Heigh-ho! that I were but wed!'

The Giant Frodge-dobbulum said to his boots,
'The first maid I meet I will wed, if she suits!'

Down came a thunderbolt, rumble and glare!
Frodge-dobbulum Castle blew up in the air.

The giant, deprived of self-control,
Was carried away to the very North Pole.

The point is so sharp it makes him shrink;
The northern streamers, they make him blink.

He blinks at the snow with its weary white;
He blinks at the spears of the northern light;

Kicks out with one boot; says, 'Fi-fo-fum!
I am the Giant Frodge-dobbulum!'

But who cares whether he is or not,
Living in such an inclement spot?

W. B. RANDS

Grim

Beside the blaze of forty fires
    Giant Grim doth sit,
Roasting a thick-wooled mountain sheep
    Upon an iron spit.
Above him wheels the winter sky,
    Beneath him, fathoms deep,
Lies hidden in the valley mists
    A village fast asleep —
Save for one restive hungry dog
    That, snuffing towards the height,
Smells Grim's broiled supper-meat, and spies
    His watch-fire twinkling bright.

WALTER DE LA MARE

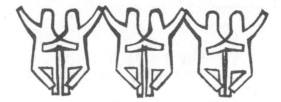

Donkey Riding

Were you ever in Quebec
Stowing timber on the deck,
Where there's a king with a golden crown
Riding on a donkey?

   Hey! ho! away we go,
   Donkey riding, donkey riding.
   Hey! ho! away we go,
   Riding on a donkey.

Were you ever off the Horn
Where it's always fine and warm,
And seen the lion and the unicorn
Riding on a donkey?

   Hey! ho! away we go,
   Donkey riding, donkey riding.
   Hey! ho! away we go,
   Riding on a donkey.

Were you ever in Cardiff Bay
Where the folks all shout 'Hooray!
Here comes John with his three months' pay
Riding on a donkey'?

   Hey! ho! away we go,
   Donkey riding, donkey riding.
   Hey! ho! away we go,
   Riding on a donkey.

5

The Rebel Soldier

One morning, one morning, one morning in May,
I heard a poor soldier lamenting and say,
I heard a poor soldier lamenting and mourn:
'I am a rebel soldier and far from my home.

'I'll eat when I'm hungry and drink when I'm dry.
If the Yankees don't kill me I'll live until I die:
If the Yankees don't kill me and cause me to mourn,
I am a rebel soldier and far from my home.

'I'll build me a castle on some green mountain high,
Where the wild geese can see me as they do pass by,
Where the wild geese can see me and hear my sad mourn:
I am a rebel soldier and far from my home.'

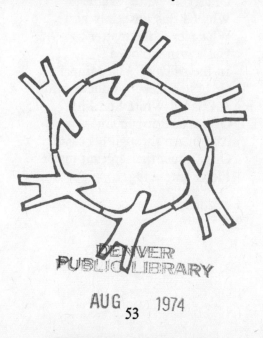

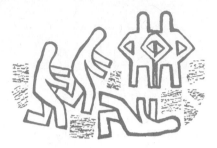

The Dashing White Sergeant

Charging down the corridors,
Pelting down the stairs,
Spinning round the corners
Knocking into chairs,
Without a 'beg your pardon'
Or, 'I didn't mean to do it!'
Unless he puts the brakes hard on
He's surely going to rue it.

What's the hurry, what's the cause
Of all this skitter-skatter?
Why all this unseemly haste,
Whatever is the matter?
Has a war exploded
In the wilds of Asia Minor?
Or has an iceberg undermined
A Cunard White Star liner?
Or has a tiger run amok
And bitten through his cage?
Or is it just the sergeant major
Flown into a rage?

Look out everybody,
Here he comes again!
His face is white as whitewash
And bedewed with beads of pain;
You can hear the rapid clatter
As he flings aside a door;
And the slither as he slides
Along the highly polished floor.
Dashing hither-thither,
At a really frantic pace;
Pheidippides of Athens
Never ran a harder race!

But don't worry, don't get anxious,
Don't let it make you ill,
It's just the sergeant's nature;
He simply can't keep still!

DAVID SHAVREEN

The Wandering Ghost

Woe's me, woe's me!
The acorn's not yet
Fallen from the tree
That's to grow the wood
That's to make the cradle
That's to rock the bairn
That's to grow a man
That's to lay me.

Choosing Their Names

Our old cat has kittens three —
What do you think their names should be?

One is a tabby, with emerald eyes,
    And a tail that's long and slender,
And into a temper she quickly flies
    If you ever by chance offend her:
        I think we shall call her this —
        I think we shall call her that —
Now, don't you think that Pepperpot
    Is a nice name for a cat?

One is black, with a frill of white,
    And her feet are all white fur, too;
If you stroke her she carries her tail upright
    And quickly begins to purr, too!
        I think we shall call her this —
        I think we shall call her that —
Now don't you think that Sootikin
    Is a nice name for a cat?

One is a tortoiseshell, yellow and black,
  With plenty of white about him;
If you tease him, at once he sets up his back:
  He's a quarrelsome one, ne'er doubt him.
    I think we shall call him this —
    I think we shall call him that —
Now don't you think that Scratchaway
  Is a nice name for a cat?

Our old cat has kittens three
And I fancy these their names will be;
Pepperpot, Sootikin, Scratchaway — there!
Were ever kittens with these to compare?
And we call the old mother —
            Now, what do you think?
Tabitha Longclaws Tiddley Wink.

THOMAS HOOD

The Ruined Nest

Hear what the mournful linnets say:
  'We built our nest compact and warm,
But cruel boys came round our way
  And took our summerhouse by storm.

'They crushed the eggs so neatly laid;
  So now we sit with drooping wing,
And watch the ruin they have made,
  Too late to build, too sad to sing.'

CHRISTINA ROSSETTI

Names for Twins

Each pair of twins,
rabbits or dogs,
children or frogs,
has to have names
that are almost the same
(to show that they're twins)
but are different too;
so here's what you do.

Find double words,
like Higgledy-Piggledy
(good names for pigs)
or Shilly and Shally
or Dilly and Dally
or Knick and Knack.

Namby and Pamby
are better for poodles;
Whing-Ding for swallows;
Misty and Moisty
and Wishy and Washy
especially for fish.
Call twin kittens
Inky and Pinky
or Helter and Skelter,
or Pell and Mell.
(It's easy to tell
they are twins if their names
have a humdrum sound.)

Crinkum and Crankum
are perfect for squirrels,
like Hanky and Panky
or Fiddle and Faddle;
but Mumbo and Jumbo
are mainly for elephants.
(Airy and Fairy
would never suit *them*.)
Willy and Nilly
will fit almost any twins.
Hubble and Bubble
or Hodge and Podge
or Roly and Poly
are mainly for fat twins.

Chitter and Chatter
or Jingle and Jangle
or Pitter and Patter,
of course, are for noisy twins.
Further than that,
there's Harum and Scarum,
or Hocus and Pocus,
or Heebie and Jeebie,
but these are peculiar,
and have to be used,
like Mixty and Maxty,
for very *odd* pairs. . . .
You see what begins
when you have to name twins.

ALASTAIR REED

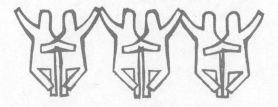

59

A Frog he went a-courting

A frog he went a-courting, he did ride
With a pistol and a sword hung by his side.

He rode up to little Mousie's door,
He off his horse and he boarded the floor.

He took Miss Mousie upon his knee,
Saying: 'Miss Mouse will you marry me?'

'O kind sir, I can't say that,
You have to ask my uncle rat.'

Uncle rat went galloping to town,
To buy his niece a wedding-gown.

Where will the wedding supper be?
Away down yonder in the hollow bush tree.

The first come in was the bumble-bee,
With his fiddle on his knee.

The next come in was an old fat goose,
He began to fiddle and she got loose.

The next come in was a little flea,
To dance a jig with the bumble-bee.

The next come in was the old tom cat,
He says: 'I'll put a stop to that.'

The goose she then flew up on the wall,
And old tom cat put a stop to it all.

Gentleman Frog swam over the lake,
And he got swallowed by a big black snake.

That is the end of one two three,
The frog, the mouse and bumble-bee.

Up in the North

Up in the north, a long way off,
The donkey's got the whooping-cough.

The Three Huntsmen

There were three jovial Welshmen,
  As I have heard men say,
And they would go a-hunting
  Upon St. David's Day.

All the day they hunted,
  And nothing did they find,
But a ship a-sailing,
  A-sailing in the wind.

One said it was a ship,
  The second, he said, Nay!
The third said it was a house
  With the chimney blown away.

And all the night they hunted,
  And nothing did they find,
But the moon a-gliding,
  And that they left behind.

One said it was the moon,
  The second, he said Nay!
The third said it was a cheese
  With half of it cut away.

And all next day they hunted,
  And nothing did they find,
But a hedgehog in a bramble,
  And that they left behind.

One said it was a hedgehog,
  The second, he said Nay!
The third, it was a pin-cushion
  With the pins stuck in the wrong way.

And all the night they hunted,
  And nothing did they find,
But a hare in a turnip field,
  And that they left behind.

One said it was a hare,
  The second, he said, Nay!
The third said it was a calf
  And the cow had run away.

And all next day they hunted,
  And nothing did they find,
But an owl in a holly-tree,
  And that they left behind.

One said it was an owl,
  The second, he said, Nay!
The third said 'twas an old man
  And his beard was growing grey.

Then all three jovial Welshmen
  Came riding home at last:
'For three days we have nothing killed,
  And never broke our fast!'

The Rivals

I heard a bird at dawn
    Singing sweetly on a tree,
That the dew was on the lawn,
    And the wind was on the lea;
But I didn't listen to him,
    For he didn't sing to me.

I didn't listen to him,
    For he didn't sing to me
That the dew was on the lawn
    And the wind was on the lea;
I was singing at the time
    Just as prettily as he.

I was singing all the time
    Just as prettily as he,
About the dew upon the lawn
    And the wind upon the lea;
So I didn't listen to him
    As he sang upon a tree.

JAMES STEPHENS

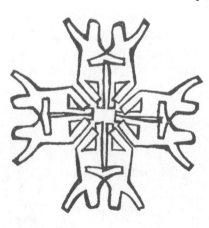

64

The Wise Men of Gotham

In a bowl to sea
Went wise men three,
　　On a brilliant night of June:
They carried a net,
And their hearts were set
　　On fishing up the moon.

Far, far at sea
Were the wise men three
　　When their fishing-net they threw;
And at the throw
The moon below
　　In a thousand fragments flew.

They drew in their net:
It was empty and wet,
　　And they had lost their pain;
Soon ceased the play
Of each dancing ray
　　And the image was round again.

The three wise men
Got home again
　　To their children and their wives;
But about their trip,
And their net's vain dip,
　　They disputed all their lives.

T. L. PEACOCK

The Bee and the Ant

The daily labours of the bee
Awake my soul to industry.
Who can observe the careful ant
And not provide for future want?

JOHN GAY

The Old Tailor

There was once an old Tailor of Hickery Mo,
Too tired at evening to sew, to sew;
He put by his needle, he snapped his thread,
And, cross-legged, sang to his fiddle instead.
His candle bobbed at each note that came
And spat out a spark from the midst of its flame;
His catgut strings they yelped and yawled,
The wilder their scrapings the louder he bawled;
The grease trickled over at every beat,
Welled down to the stick in a winding-sheet —
Till up sprang Puss from the fire, with a wow!
'A *fine* kakkamangul you're making now!'

WALTER DE LA MARE

Tailor

I saw a little Tailor sitting stitch, stitch, stitching
Cross-legged on the floor of his kitch, kitch, kitchen.
His thumbs and his fingers were so nim, nim, nimble
With his wax and his scissors and his thim, thim, thimble.

His silk and his cotton he was thread, thread, threading
For a gown and a coat for a wed, wed, wedding,
His needle flew as swift as a swal, swal, swallow,
And his spools and his reels had to fol, fol, follow.

He hummed as he worked a merry dit, dit, ditty:
'The Bride is as plump as she's pret, pret, pretty,
I wouldn't have her taller or short, short, shorter,
She can laugh like the falling of wat, wat, water,

'She can put a cherry-pie, togeth, geth, gether,
She can dance as light as a feath, feath, feather,
She can sing as sweet as a fid, fid, fiddle,
And she's only twenty inches round the mid, mid, middle.'

The happy little Tailor went on stitch, stitch, stitching
The black and the white in his kitch, kitch, kitchen.
He will wear the black one, she will wear the white one,
And the knot the Parson ties will be a tight, tight, tight one.

ELEANOR FARJEON

67

Rattle Snake

A nice young ma-wa-wan
Lived on a hi-wi-will;
A nice young ma-wa-wan,
For I knew him we-we-well.

This nice young ma-wa-wan
Went out to mo-wo-wow
To see if he-we-we
Could make a sho-wo-wow.

He scarce had mo-wo-wowed
Half round the fie-we-wield
Till a rattle sna-wa-wake
Come and bit him on the he-we-weel.

He laid right dow-wo-wown
Upon the gro-wo-wound
And shut his ey-wy-wyes
And looked all aro-wo-wound.

'O pappy da-wa-wad,
Go tell my ga-wa-wal,
That I'm a-goin' ter di-wi-wie,
For I know I sha-wa-wall.

'O pappy da-wa-wad,
Go spread the new-wew-wews;
And here come Sa-wa-wall
Without her sho-woo-woos.'

'O John, O Joh-wa-wahn,
Why did you go-wo-wo
Way down in the mea-wea-weadow
So far to mo-wo-wow?'

'O Sal, O sa-wa-wal,
Why don't you kno-wo-wow
When the grass gets ri-wi-wipe,
It must be mo-wo-wowed?'

Come all young gir-wir-wirls
And shed a te-we-wear
For this young ma-wa-wan
That died right he-we-were.

Come all young me-we-wen
And warning ta-wa-wake
And don't get bi-wi-wit
By a rattle sna-wa-wake.

The Pobble who has no Toes

The pobble who has no toes
   Had once as many as we;
When they said, 'Some day you may lose them all',
   He replied — 'Fish fiddle-de-dee!'
And his Aunt Jobiska made him drink
Lavender water tinged with pink,
For she said, 'The world in general knows
There's nothing so good for a Pobble's toes!'

The Pobble who has no toes
   Swam across the Bristol Channel;
But before he set out he wrapped his nose
   In a piece of scarlet flannel.
For his Aunt Jobiska said, 'No harm
Can come to his toes if his nose is warm;
And it's perfectly known that a Pobble's toes
Are safe, — provided he minds his nose.'

The Pobble swam fast and well,
   And when boats or ships came near him,
He tinkledy-blinkledy-winkled a bell,
   So that all the world could hear him.
And all the Sailors and Admirals cried,
When they saw him nearing the further side, —
'He has gone to fish, for his Aunt Jobiska's
Runcible cat with crimson whiskers!'

But before he touched the shore,
  The shore of the Bristol Channel,
A sea-green Porpoise carried away
  His wrapper of scarlet flannel.
And when he came to observe his feet,
Formerly garnished with toes so neat,
His face at once became forlorn
On perceiving that all his toes were gone!

And nobody ever knew,
  From that dark day to the present,
Whoso had taken the Pobble's toes,
  In a manner so far from pleasant.
Whether the shrimps or crawfish grey,
Or crafty mermaids stole them away—
Nobody knew; and nobody knows
How the Pobble was robbed of his twice five toes!

The Pobble who has no toes
  Was placed in a friendly Bark,
And they rowed him back, and carried him up
  To his Aunt Jobiska's Park.
And she made him a feast at his earnest wish
Of eggs and buttercups fried with fish;—
And she said,—'It's a fact the whole world knows,
That Pobbles are happier without their toes.'

EDWARD LEAR

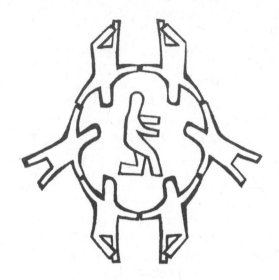

The Little Girl Lost

... Seven summers old
Lovely Lyca told;
She had wandered long
Hearing wild birds' song.

'Sweet sleep, come to me
Underneath this tree.
Do father, mother, weep?
Where can Lyca sleep?

'Lost in desert wild
Is your little child.
How can Lyca sleep
If her mother weep?

'If her heart does ache
Then let Lyca wake;
If my mother sleep,
Lyca shall not weep.

'Frowning, frowning night,
O'er this desert bright,
Let thy moon arise
While I close my eyes.'

Sleeping Lyca lay
While the beasts of prey,
Come from caverns deep,
Viewed the maid asleep.

The kingly lion stood,
And the virgin viewed,
Then he gambolled round
O'er the hallowed ground.

Leopards, tigers, play
Round her as she lay,
While the lion old
Bowed his mane of gold

And her bosom lick,
And upon her neck
From his eyes of flame
Ruby tears there came;

While the lioness
Loosed her slender dress,
And naked they conveyed
To caves the sleeping maid.

WILLIAM BLAKE

The Little Girl Found

All the night in woe
Lyca's parents go
Over valleys deep,
While the deserts weep.

Tired and woe-begone,
Hoarse with making moan,
Arm in arm seven days
They traced the desert ways.

Seven nights they sleep
Among shadows deep,
And dream they see their child
Starved in desert wild.

Pale, through pathless ways
The fancied image strays
Famished, weeping, weak,
With hollow piteous shriek.

Rising from unrest,
The trembling woman pressed
With feet of weary woe:
She could no further go.

In his arms he bore
Her, armed with sorrow sore;
Till before their way
A couching lion lay.

Turning back was vain:
Soon his heavy mane
Bore them to the ground.
Then he stalked around,

Smelling to his prey;
But their fears allay
When he licks their hands,
And silent by them stands.

They look upon his eyes
Filled with deep surprise;
And wondering behold
A spirit armed in gold.

On his head a crown;
On his shoulders down
Flowed his golden hair.
Gone was all their care.

'Follow me,' he said;
'Weep not for the maid;
In my palace deep
Lyca lies asleep.'

Then they followéd
Where the vision led,
And saw their sleeping child
Among tigers wild.

To this day they dwell
In a lonely dell;
Nor fear the wolfish howl
Nor the lions' growl.

WILLIAM BLAKE

Nobodies

I'm nobody! Who are you?
Are you nobody, too?
Then there's a pair of us—don't tell!
They'd banish us, you know.

How dreary to be somebody!
How public, like a frog
To tell your name the livelong day
To an admiring bog!

EMILY DICKINSON

A Christmas Carol

The other night
I saw a light!
    A star as bright as day!
And ever among
A maiden sung:
    'By-by, baby, lullay.'

This virgin clear
Who had no peer
    Unto her son did say,
'I pray thee, son,
Grant me a boon
    To sing by-by, lullay.

'Let child or man,
Whoever can
    Be merry on this day,
And blessings bring—
So I shall sing
    "By-by, baby, lullay." '

(ABOUT 1500)

77

The Lost Shoe

Poor little Lucy
  By some mischance
Lost her shoe
  As she did dance:
'Twas not on the stairs,
  Not in the hall;
Not where they sat
  At supper at all.
She looked in the garden,
  But there it was not;
Henhouse, or kennel,
  Or high dovecote.
Dairy and meadow,
  And wild woods through
Showed not a trace
  Of Lucy's shoe.
Bird nor bunny
  Nor glimmering moon
Breathed a whisper
  Of where 'twas gone.
It was cried and cried,
  Oyez and Oyez!

In French, Dutch, Latin,
    In Portuguese.
Ships the dark seas
    Went plunging through,
But none brought news
    Of Lucy's shoe.
And still she patters
    In silk and leather,
O'er snow, sand, shingle,
    In every weather;
Spain, and Africa,
    Hindustan,
Java, China,
    And lamped Japan;
Plain and desert,
    She hops — hops through,
Pernambuco
    To gold Peru;
Mountain and forest,
    And river too,
All the world over
    For her lost shoe.

WALTER DE LA MARE

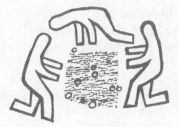

The Jolly Beggar

There was a jolly beggar,
　　He had a wooden leg,
Lame from his cradle,
　　And forced to beg.

A bag for his oatmeal,
　　Another for his salt,
And a long pair of crutches
　　To show that he can halt.

A bag for his wheat,
　　Another for his rye,
And a little bottle by his side
　　To drink when he's a-dry.

'Seven years I begged
　　For my old master Wilde;
He taught me to beg
　　When I was but a child.

'I begged for my master,
　　And got him store of pelf,
But goodness now be praised,
　　I'm begging for myself.

'In a hollow tree
　　I live, and pay no rent,
Providence provides for me,
　　And I am well content.

'Of all the occupations
   A beggar's is the best,
For whenever he's a-weary,
   He can lay him down to rest.

'I fear no plots against me,
   I live in open cell:
Then who would be a king, lads,
   When a beggar lives so well?'

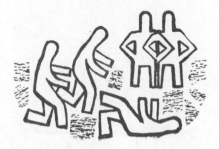

Titania's Sleeping-place

I know a bank whereon the wild thyme blows,
Where oxlips and the nodding violet grows;
Quite over-canopied with lush woodbine,
With sweet musk-roses, and with eglantine:
There sleeps Titania sometime of the night,
Lulled in these flowers with dances and delight;
And there the snake throws her enamelled skin,
Weed wide enough to wrap a fairy in.

WILLIAM SHAKESPEARE

weed, clothing

The Conjuror

The cards, obedient to his words,
Are by a fillip turned to birds.
He shakes his bag, he shows all fair,
His fingers spread, and nothing there—
Then bids it rain with showers of gold!
And now his ivory eggs are told,
But when from thence the hen he draws,
Amazed spectators hum applause.

JOHN GAY

told, counted

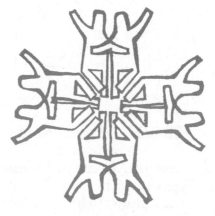

End of Term

One more day of sin,
One more day of sorrow,
One more day in this old hole,
We're staying home tomorrow!

Robin

With a bonfire throat,
Legs of twig,
A dark brown coat,
The inspector robin
Comes where I dig.

Military man
With a bright eye
And a wooden leg,
He must scrounge and beg
Now the summer's by:

Beg at the doors,
Scrounge in the gardens,
While daylight lessens
And the grass glistens
And the ground hardens.

The toads have their vaults,
The squirrels their money,
The swifts their journey;
For him the earth's anger,
The taste of hunger.

And his unfrightened song
For the impending snows
Is also for the rose
And for the great Armada
And the Phoenician trader
And the last missile raider —
It's the only one he knows.

HAL SUMMERS

83

Topsyturvey-World

If the butterfly courted the bee,
  And the owl the porcupine;
If churches were built in the sea,
  And three times one was nine;
If the pony rode his master,
  If the buttercups ate the cows,
If the cat stopped being the master
  And was hunted, sir, by the mouse;

If mother, sir, sold the baby
  To a gipsy for half-a-crown;
If a gentleman, sir, was a lady,
  The world would be Upside-Down!
If any or all of these wonders
  Should ever come about,
I should not consider them blunders,
  For I should be Inside-Out!

W. B. RANDS

Gulliver in Lilliput

From his nose
Clouds he blows.
When he speaks,
Thunder breaks.
When he eats,
Famine threats.
When he treads,
Mountains' heads
Groan and shake;
Armies quake.
See him stride
Valleys wide,
Over woods,
Over floods.
Troops take heed,
Man and steed:
Left and right,
Speed your flight!
In amaze
Lost I gaze
Toward the skies:
See! and believe your eyes!

ALEXANDER POPE

A Grace from Scotland

Some hae meat that canna eat
   And some could eat that want it;
But we hae meat and we can eat,
   For which the Lord be thankit!

Father William

'You are old, Father William,' the young man said,
  'And your hair has become very white;
And yet you incessantly stand on your head —
  Do you think, at your age, it is right?'

'In my youth,' Father William replied to his son,
  'I feared it might injure the brain;
But, now that I'm perfectly sure I have none,
  Why, I do it again and again.'

'You are old,' said the youth, 'as I mentioned before,
  And have grown most uncommonly fat;
Yet you turned a back-somersault in at the door —
  Pray, what is the reason of that?'

'In my youth,' said the sage, as he shook his grey locks,
  'I kept all my limbs very supple
By the use of this ointment — one shilling the box —
  Allow me to sell you a couple?'

'You are old,' said the youth, 'and your jaws are too weak
  For anything tougher than suet;
Yet you finished the goose, with the bones and the beak —
  Pray, how did you manage to do it?'

'In my youth,' said his father, 'I took to the law,
  And argued each case with my wife;
And the muscular strength which it gave to my jaw
  Has lasted the rest of my life.'

'You are old,' said the youth, 'one would hardly suppose
  That your eye was as steady as ever;
Yet you balanced an eel on the end of your nose —
  What made you so awfully clever?'

'I have answered three questions, and that is enough,'
    Said his father. 'Don't give yourself airs!
Do you think I can listen all day to such stuff?
    Be off, or I'll kick you down-stairs!'

LEWIS CARROLL

Fine Weather for Ducks

As ice-cream cartons float in the drain,
The beach-stalls lose and the cinemas gain,
For holiday-makers hate the rain—
    Unlike the ducks and William Roy.

In mac, sou'wester and gum-boots, he
Stands under spouts, shakes a wet tree,
Leaps into puddles: it never can be
    Too wet for the ducks or William Roy.

The ducks come into their own. They tack
And splash and paddle and waddle and quack:
'Three cheers for rain! The fine weather's back!'
    So think the ducks and one small boy.

RAYMOND O'MALLEY

The Wind

Which way does the Wind come? What way does he go?
He rides over the water, and over the snow,
Through wood, and through vale; and, o'er rocky height
Which the goat cannot climb, takes his sounding flight.
He tosses about in every bare tree,
As, if you look up, you plainly may see;
But how he will come, and whither he goes,
There's never a scholar in England knows.

DOROTHY WORDSWORTH

Peace

And he shall judge among many people,
And rebuke strong nations afar off;
And they shall beat their swords into plowshares,
And their spears into pruninghooks:
Nation shall not lift up a sword against nation,
Neither shall they learn war any more.
But they shall sit every man under his vine
And under his fig tree;
And none shall make them afraid:
For the mouth of the Lord of hosts has spoken it.
For all people will walk every one in the name of his god,
And we will walk in the name of the Lord our God
    for ever and ever.

THE BIBLE

The Streets of Laredo

As I walked out in the streets of Laredo,
  As I walked out in Laredo one day,
I spied a poor cowboy wrapped up in white linen,
  Wrapped up in white linen and as cold as the clay.

'I see by your outfit that you are a cowboy,'
  These words he did say as I boldly stepped by.
'Come, sit down beside me and hear my sad story;
  I was shot in the breast and I know I must die.

'Once in my saddle I used to look handsome,
  Once in my saddle I used to look gay.
I first went to drinking and then to card-playing,
  Got shot in the breast, which ended my day.

'Let sixteen gamblers come handle my coffin,
  Let sixteen girls come carry my pall;
Put bunches of roses all over my coffin,
  Put roses to deaden the clods as they fall.

'And beat the drum slowly and play the fife lowly,
  And beat the dead march as you carry me along;
Take me to the prairie and lay the turf o'er me,
  For I'm a young cowboy and I know I've done wrong.'

We beat the drum slowly and we played the fife lowly,
  And bitterly wept as we bore him along;
For we all loved our comrade, so brave, young and handsome,
  We loved the young cowboy, although he'd done wrong.

Cat!

Scat!
Atter her, atter her,
Sleeky flatterer,
Spitfire chatterer,
Scatter her, scatter her
Off her mat!
Wuff!
Wuff!
Treat her rough!
Git her, git her,
Whiskery spitter!
Catch her, catch her,
Green-eyed scratcher!
Slathery
Slithery
Hisser,
Don't miss her!
Run till you're dithery,
Hithery
Thithery
Pfitts! pfitts!
How she spits!
Spitch! Spatch!
Can't she scratch!
Scritching the bark
Of the sycamore-tree,
She's reached her ark
And's hissing at me
Pfitts! pfitts!
Wuff! wuff!
Scat,
Cat!
That's
That!

ELEANOR FARJEON

A Dis, A Dis

A dis, a dis o' green grass,
    A daisy dis, a dis!
Come all you pretty maidens
    And dance along with this.
And you shall have a duck so blue,
    And you shall have a drake,
And you shall have a pretty young man
    A-dancing for your sake.

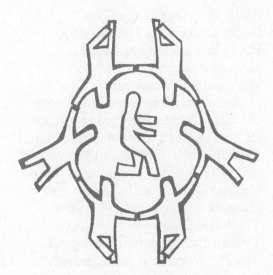

The Hippocrump

Along the valley of the Ump
Gallops the fearful Hippocrump.
His hide is leathery and thick;
His eyelids open with a *Click!*
His mouth he closes with a *Clack!*
He has three humps upon his back;
On each of these there grows a score
Of horny spikes, and sometimes more.
His hair is curly, thick and brown;
Beneath his chin a beard hangs down.
He has eight feet with hideous claws;
His neck is long—and O his jaws!
The boldest falters in his track
To hear those hundred teeth go *Clack!*
The Hippocrump is fierce indeed,
But if he eats the baneful weed
That grows beside the Purple Lake,
His hundred teeth begin to ache.
Then how the creature stamps and roars
Along the Ump's resounding shores!

The drowsy cattle faint with fright;
The birds fall flat, the fish turn white.
Even the rocks begin to shake;
The children in their beds awake;
The old ones quiver, quail, and quake.
'Alas!' they cry. 'Make no mistake,
It is *Himself* — he's got the Ache
From eating by the Purple Lake!'
Some say, 'It is *Old You-know-who* —
He's in a rage: what shall we do?'
'Lock up the barns, protect the stores,
Bring all the pigs and sheep indoors!'

They call upon their god, Agw-ump,
To save them from the Hippocrump.
'What's that I hear go hop-skip-jump?
He's coming! Stand aside there!' *Bump!*
Lump-lump! — 'He's on the bridge now!' — *Lump!*
'I hear his tail' — *ker-flump, ker-flump!*
'I see the prickles on his hump!
It *is*, it *IS* — the Hippocrump!
Defend us now, O Great Agw-ump!'

Thus prayed the dwellers by the Ump.
Their prayer was heard. A broken stump
Caught the intruder in the rump.
He slipped into the foaming river,
Whose icy water quenched his fever,
Then while the creature floundering lay,
The timid people ran away;
And when the morrow dawned serene
The Hippocrump was no more seen.
Glad hymns of joy the people raised:
'For ever Great Agw-ump be praised!'

JAMES REEVES

Creatures in the Night

The owl is abroad, the bat, and the toad,
    And so is the cat-a-mountain;
The ant and the mole sit both in a hole,
    And the frog peeps out o' the fountain.

BEN JONSON

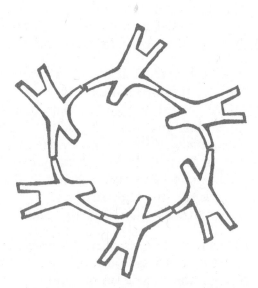

The Haystack

Too dense to have a door,
Window or fireplace or a floor,
They saw this cottage up,
Huge bricks of grass, clover and buttercup
Carting to byre and stable,
Where cow and horse will eat wall, roof and gable.

ANDREW YOUNG

'Old Zip Coon' he played all day,
Until the natives ran away;
He played and played by the light of the moon,
Till they wished they had never heard of 'Old Zip Coon'.

They have left him there by the deep blue sea,
Where he lives alone in a hollow tree;
And he plays that tune and it never ends,
So it isn't surprising that he has no friends.

'Old Zip Coon' he plays all day,
There's no one left to run away;
And still he thinks it's a beautiful tune,
And that is the history of 'Old Zip Coon'.

DAVID STEVENS

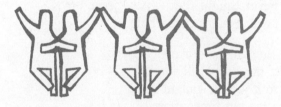

The Starlings

Early in spring time, on raw and windy mornings,
Beneath the freezing house-eaves I heard the starlings sing –
'Ah dreary March month, is this then a time for building wearily?
  Sad, sad, to think that the year is but begun.'

Late in the autumn, on still and cloudless evenings,
Among the golden reed-beds I heard the starlings sing –
'Ah that sweet March month, when we and our mates were
    courting merrily;
  Sad, sad, to think that the year is all but done.'

CHARLES KINGSLEY

Greenland Fishery

'Twas in eighteen hundred and fifty three,
And of June the thirteenth day,
That our gallant ship her anchor weighed,
And for Greenland bore away, brave boys,
And for Greenland bore away.

The look-out in the cross-trees stood,
With his spy-glass in his hand.
'There's a whale, there's a whale, there's a whale-fish,' he cried,
'And she blows at every span, brave boys,
And she blows at every span!'

We struck that whale, the line paid out,
But she gave a flourish with her tail;
The boat capsized and four men were drowned,
And we never caught that whale, brave boys,
And we never caught that whale.

'To lose the whale,' our captain said,
'It grieves my heart full sore;
But oh! to lose four gallant men,
It grieves me ten times more, brave boys,
It grieves me ten times more.'

Index of First Lines

ACKNOWLEDGEMENTS

The editors make grateful acknowledgement to the following for permission to reprint copyright material:

Mrs H. M. Davies and Jonathan Cape Ltd for 'In the Snow' from the *Collected Poems* of W. H. Davies; The Literary Trustees of Walter de la Mare and the Society of Authors as their representative for 'Please to Remember', 'Grim', 'The Old Tailor' and 'The Lost Shoe'; Harvard University Press for a poem from *The Poems of Emily Dickinson*; J. J. du Preez for Elizabeth du Preez's 'The Kitten'; David Higham Associates Ltd for 'Anne 1702' from *Kings and Queens*, 'Scarecrow' from *Country Child's Alphabet*, and 'Cat' and 'Tailor' from *Then There Were Three* by Eleanor Farjeon; The Trustees of the Hardy Estate and Macmillan & Co Ltd for 'The Robin' from *The Collected Poems of Thomas Hardy*; Basil Blackwell for 'The Toad' and 'Useful Things' by Mrs E. L. M. King; Ogden Nash and Curtis Brown Ltd for 'The Ostrich' from *You Can't Get There From Here*; The Clarendon Press for 'End of Term' from *Language and Lore of Schoolchildren* by Iona and Peter Opie; J. M. Dent & Sons Ltd for 'Names for Twins' from *Ounce, Dice, Trice* by Alastair Reed; James Reeves and Oxford University Press for 'Things to Remember' from *The Blackbird in the Lilac*; James Reeves and William Heinemann Ltd for 'Mr. Tom Narrow' from *The Wandering Moon* and 'The Hippocrump' from *Prefabulous Animiles*; David Shavreen for 'The Dashing White Sergeant'; Mrs Iris Wise and Macmillan & Co Ltd for 'White Fields' and 'The Rivals' from the *Collected Poems* of James Stephens; Hal Summers for 'The Robin'; John Walsh and Oxford University Press for 'On These November Evenings' from *The Roundabout by the Sea*; John Walsh and William Heinemann Ltd for 'The Sandcastle' from *The Truants*; Rupert Hart-Davis Ltd for 'The Haystack' from the *Collected Poems* of Andrew Young.